BEYOND THE WALLS 2024

Beyond the walls

New Writing From York St John University 2024

LENDAL PRESS

First published in 2024 by Lendal Press
an imprint of Valley Press
Woodend, The Crescent, Scarborough, UK, YO11 2PW

ISBN 978-1-915606-43-3
Cat. no. LP0019

'The Oversoul' (p84) includes lines from *The Upanishads*
as translated by Juan Mascaro (Penguin Classics, 1965).

Printed and bound in Great Britain by
Imprint Digital, Upton Pyne, Exeter.

Contents

Foreword

What has brought you, reader, beyond the walls?

If you have bought this book, it is likely you are a student at York St John, or the parent, grandparent, or friend of one. Perhaps you are a devotee of Valley Press, and are growing your collection of their slim, meticulous volumes. It could be years from now, in a charity shop of a windblown seaside town, when a flash of white and a pair of opening lips catch your attention. The corners are worn, the matte a little scuffed.

We imagine you share an appetite for new writing and undiscovered voices, the levity and vitality of a debut. The work within this anthology laments a nine to five, transforms under a full moon and lays loved ones to rest. Some pieces may break your heart as their narrators endure all the vulnerability of the human body and mind. It is this impulse to manage adversity through creativity which gives cause for hope in an age of disinformation and passivity. To record what is painful, or wrongful, or previously left unsaid is a vital act of empathy.

Wherever and whenever you are, we hope you recognise yourself within these pages, it has been a pleasure to bring them to you.

The Editorial and Production Team

Over recent years, we have seen how the digital world has helped to amplify the voices of the silenced, to create solidarity across vast distances, or to combat loneliness, the 'silent killer', as it is often referred to in the media. It is timely then that the theme of this year's Beyond the Walls anthology is 'Unspoken', a theme that highlights literature's role in shining a light on what goes unsaid. Writers have always developed methods to say what cannot be said. During the Cold War, poets from Eastern Europe devised ingenious ways of using metaphor to evade censorship, to give voice to what would be silenced. Be it visions of the future, the voices of marginalised individuals, or the feelings we dare not speak about for fear of shame or exclusion, this anthology brings new voices to the literature of the unspoken. It represents the culmination of months of hard work by a group of students who have worked tirelessly as editors, designers, podcasters, marketeers, and event organisers. As the weeks went by, it was a privilege to hear the voices of those who worked on and led this year's Beyond the Walls anthology growing louder in volume. Their vision, leadership, and creativity has led to the curation of a remarkable body of work that is expanded on by a series of podcasts that probe and deepen the theme of the unspoken with guest speakers. The stories, poems and artwork created by students on YSJ's Creative Writing programmes are testament to the rich tradition of making the unheard heard, and the invisible visible. Here is a body of work that interrogates the effect of keeping silent and pursues the written word's ability to transform our surroundings and inspire our future.

Dr John Challis
Lecturer in Creative Writing
York St John University

A Ticking Clock

The sound of stifled coughs, clacking keyboards and exasperated sighs filled the quiet floor of the university library. Jas sat down in a vacant seat, pulled her battered old laptop from her tote bag (her favourite one, with the Jane Austen quote on it) and pressed the power button. Her laptop screen lit up white, then settled on the generic screensaver she couldn't be bothered to change – a landscape picture of somewhere in Greece, with stacked white villas and a sky streaked with purples, pinks and oranges. She clicked away from the picture and opened her essay plan. The essay plan in question was a series of vague bullet points; it was her desperate attempt at making a start on the 2,500 words due in the next day. Jas had decided to come to the library on her friend Ivy's advice in a last-ditch effort to not fail the module.

Twenty-three and a half hours to go.

Jas read through her shitty essay plan and sighed loudly, resting her chin in her hands and contemplating the life choices that had led her here. An alert popped up on her Instagram tab that was always open in the background, a welcome distraction from the pain of her unwritten essay. She clicked on the tab and froze when she saw who she had a private message from.

Steph.Addaman: hi

Jas immediately began to sweat. Stephanie Addaman. Jas had lectures with her, and they had a vague, polite friendship which didn't usually go outside the classroom. Steph was one of those students with an abundance of questions and thoughts on all the various forms of literature they studied. Jas was the complete opposite, always struggling to find meaning in the work and staying silent in most discussions to avoid embarrassment. She was quite jealous of Steph in that respect. There were, of course, other things Jas was jealous of, too. Like the way Steph's tightly curled hair always sat perfectly, or the way the sunlight made her eyes look like amber, or the way her boyfriend kissed her after classes …

Jas blinked, snapping herself back out of her distracted daydream. She clicked away from the tab, trying to regain her focus despite her fluttering heartbeat. The pop-up alert had disappeared from the top of her screen and she'd purposely left her phone in her bag to avoid falling into an endless loop of scrolling through reels and TikToks. Jas turned up the lo-fi music which was supposed to help concentration, and returned to the task at hand, opening up her browser and typing in the name of her preferred academic website. Academic scrolling was at least marginally more productive than social media scrolling, despite both yielding similar results of zero words written. Jas typed in some keywords from her essay plan and instantly felt overwhelmed by the amount of results – too many to read in such a short space of time. She twirled a strand of her dead-straight hair around her index finger as her eyes scanned abstract after abstract, searching for some tiny speck of inspiration. Another Instagram pop up tore her away from the task at hand, the same username taking up every thought in her mind:

Steph.Addaman

Jas' heart jumped out of her chest with a mixture of surprise and immediate anxiety. This time the curiosity was too much to bear and she needed to know what Steph had sent her. Unrealistic messages confessing a secret crush or the breakdown of her relationship buzzed through her delusional mind as she retrieved her phone from its banishment, eagerly tapping in her passcode. Her mouth felt dry as she typed out her totally casual response to Steph's messages.

Steph.Addaman: hi
Steph.Addaman: are you at uni rn
Jassy_Chandra: Hi
Jassy_Chandra: I'm in the library atm, why?
Steph.Addaman: omw 2 mins
Steph.Addaman: which floor
Jassy_Chandra: Quiet floor

Jas felt sick. Her stomach twisted up into an anxious knot and her hands felt clammy. She opened her camera to check her eyeliner hadn't smudged (it had) and that there wasn't any food in her teeth (there was). She huffed into her hand to check her breath, but wasn't certain of the result, so dug in her tote bag for the almost-empty packet of chewing gum that had been there all year. She shoved the last two stale pieces in her mouth just as the library doors creaked from across the floor, her internal panic reaching its apex as Steph's dark hair bounced into view. Jas watched her as she scanned the room, almost scared to catch her attention, scared of what this girl could possibly want from her. She knew she was being ridiculous, but what if …

Finally, Steph spotted her, and her lips which had been pursed in concentration stretched into a warm smile as she approached Jas' table.

"Hi!" She whispered enthusiastically as she sat, dumping her own tote bag unceremoniously on the table with a loud clunk.

"Hey," Jas replied, trying to seem nonchalant but dying inside. For a moment all Jas could think about was how good Steph smelt – a musky, floral scent which matched her perfectly.

"I hope you don't mind, but I lost some of my notes from the Brontë seminar – can I borrow yours?"

"Um, yeah, sure." Jas retrieved her folder from her tote bag, handing it to Steph. Their fingers brushed, and Jas felt her cheeks flush. "Should be in there."

Steph didn't acknowledge the blushing, and Jas felt a pang of disappointment, despite also not wanting Steph to notice. Steph set the folder on the table in front of her, flicking through until she found what she was looking for. Jas pretended to read an article on her laptop whilst sneaking glances at the gentle curve of Steph's neck, the line of her jaw …

I should tell her.

No, I shouldn't.

What would I say?

Your boyfriend sucks and you should date me instead?

She'd laugh at me.

I don't even know if she likes girls.

Jas chewed her gum harder. Steph took out her phone, taking pictures of Jas' notes.

"Thanks so much!" Steph closed the folder, passing it back to Jas. "I'll see you later."

Jas gave her a polite smile in reply as she stood up, slung her tote bag back over her shoulder, and turned to leave.

Do it!

"Hey, Steph," Jas called, surprised by her own sudden confidence.

Steph glanced back at her expectantly, and Jas' confidence evaporated in a heartbeat. She opened her mouth but the words lodged themselves in her throat, refusing to budge.

"Um."

Steph tilted her head patiently, her round, soft eyes lit up by the library's fluorescents. Jas felt the words shrink, shrivelling up and dying where they became stuck as the doubt settled in. She swallowed hard, sending their carcasses down into the pit of her stomach, where they would be buried, forever silenced.

"Are you going to the social next week?"

"Yeah, are you?"

"Yeah, see you then."

Jas watched her disappear through the library doors then turned back to the laptop screen glaring at her. She clicked on one of the many academic articles littering the screen and tried to force herself to read through the excessively pretentious piece of writing. Her brain and body already felt exhausted and she still hadn't written a word.

Twenty-two hours to go.

Ellen Dawson

Confessional

For the stars themselves could not outshine you,
my most beloved fire.
I could gaze at the sky in search of holy light
Or behold divine beauty in your eyes.
Fell me to fuel the pyre of your love
And I will fall to my knees in worship.
Wage holy war upon my heart
And I will relish in your divine retribution.

Barefoot in the kitchen, I touch faith,
Dancing in the moonlight,
So holy, so mortal.
I say my rosary in your name,
Praise dripping from my lips like sweet summer wine.
My Venus, bathe me in the aphros,
Let me fan you with the frond of a date palm,
And comb alabaster oil through your locks of platinum.

Reach into the clandestine corners of my soul
And offer me your absolution, my love.
In a sanctuary of whispered desires,
Our secret hymn will echo in the halls of eternity.

Chloe Farminer-Bache

They're Here

I wake up with a crick in my neck. I stretch my arms above my head, languid, groaning in satisfaction at the familiar pull of sleepy muscles. Beside me, she sleeps. Hair fanning across her face, lips parted softly. I want to kiss her, but I don't want to wake her. I settle for idly grazing my thumb down her bare arm, the softest touch, just enough.

I pull myself up, bedsheets resting just below my waist. My t-shirt is askew, twisted in my sleep, almost back to front. I take it off and throw it across the room, onto the heap of dirty laundry that is steadily piling up in the corner. I turn my head to look at my alarm clock, only just registering the time when a sharp pain paralyses my movement. I wince, instinctively reaching a hand up to cradle my neck where it hurts. I must have slept at an odd angle.

I get out of bed, the floorboards cold on the soles of my feet. In the bedside drawer, a pair of winter socks. I pull them on, flexing my toes against the soft wool, and pad across the bedroom, footsteps silent. She is snoring gently, endearingly.

In the bathroom, I turn on the light. It's a pull cord, makes a satisfying 'click' sound as I tug at it. My face is illuminated in the mirror. Blotchy skin, sleep crusted around the eyes, cracked lips. I ignore my flaws and splash my face with lukewarm water; I never let the tap run long enough to get hot. As I bend down, the phantom pain is there again. I massage the muscles in my neck with deft fingers, hoping to loosen a knot.

Brushing my teeth is a ritual. I gargle mouthwash, and spit it into the sink, minty splatters across the ceramic. Best not forget to rinse it out; she hates when I leave a mess. I run the tap again. The water is steaming now.

Downstairs, I feed the cats. They meow at me expectantly, weaving in between my legs, heads butting my calves in an equal display of insistence and affection. For breakfast, I eat a bowl of cereal topped with banana slices and oat milk and wash it down with a black coffee.

I feel more alert. The crick in my neck persists. She begins to stir in the bedroom. I hear the bed frame squeak as she gets up, then a few moments later, the telltale flush of the toilet. I'm beginning my workday, poised at my desk, my laptop open on 56 unread emails. I delete them all without reading them.

'Hi,' She appears in the doorway. She looks soft. I take her into my arms and kiss her face. It would be too easy to get distracted, to pull her into my lap, touch her in ways only I can. Before I can slip my hand under her pyjama top, she pulls back, chastises me. 'Later.'

Later comes. Eight hours of work done, if it can be called work. My official title is Telephone Sales Representative, which is corporate babble for cold caller. She cooks, we eat dinner in comfortable silence, I wash the dishes. I don't mention the pain in my neck, which has now travelled further down my side, encroaching my collarbone and sternum.

She takes me to bed and we make love. Afterwards, I turn on my side, her fingers dancing down my spine. I don't tell her that it hurts, when she grazes my shoulder blades. Instead, I chew on my bottom lip and try to relax under her touch.

If she notices my stiffness, she says nothing.

In the middle of the night, I wake with a start. My heart rate is sky high – a bad dream, perhaps. I can't remember much of it, but my chest is slick with sweat and my breathing laboured. She doesn't wake up, has always been the better sleeper. I move to sit up, but the pain is now in my stomach, and my hips. My head is as heavy as a bowling ball when I try to lift it from the pillow. I open my mouth to speak, to get her attention, but all that comes out is a garbled string of nonsense. My brain is thinking the words, but there's something wrong with the synapses. The information can't get out. I try again. I am wailing.

She wakes up slowly. She rolls over and bores her gaze into my side profile. I am laying on my back. I can't move anything.

'What is it, darling?' She says, sickly sweet. She is smiling. I can hear it in her voice. 'You can tell me.'

I *can't* and she knows it. I am immobile, mute, and terrified. Everything hurts. I wail again, feel hot tears against my cheeks.

She uses the sleeve of her pyjama top to wipe them away.

'Don't cry, it's all going to be fine.'

Then, 'I had to do it, darling.'

The realisation hits me like a ton of bricks. Dinner, last night.

The night before. She always cooks. I never questioned why. 'It's just a simple neuromuscular blocker. I wouldn't hurt you.' Her tone conveys a sense of pride steeped in irony. She is hurting me, in ways I never imagined she would. I want to ask her why she did it, what she's going to do next. But I'm trapped inside my own body, clawing to get out. There is a knock at the door. She squeals excitedly. 'They're here!'

They, whoever *they* are, traipse muddy boots into our bedroom. They lift me ungraciously onto a stretcher and I am carried out of my home. With what little movement I have of my eyes, I find her. She stares at me, unwavering. I love her so much, and this is what I get for it.

I don't know who she is. I don't know why she has betrayed me. All I know is the pain, and the fear, and the unknown.

I close my eyes.

Jess Hodgson

The Riverboat Affair

"How you doing?" Simon shouted this over his shoulder, his voice full of laughter. He was clearly enjoying himself. She glared at his back. The sweat soaking his shirt was starting to resemble a heart. Even his clothing was mocking her.

"Fine," she called back. Maggie bit her lip as she gripped the handlebars even tighter, trying to keep up with him and stay on the trail. The narrow, overgrown track taunted her with every twist and turn, every jolt and jar. Nettles flicked at her arms and legs leaving stinging welts as souvenirs and brambles clawed at her with their spiteful barbs. Even though the sun was shining, all she could see were the shadows crawling along the uneven ground in front of her trembling wheel.

She winced as another thorny stem made a grab for her ankle. She tried to look down to see if there was any blood. As she wobbled then righted herself, Maggie questioned why she was there. It was Sunday afternoon, normally a time for papers and a pint or an old black and white film. But not this Sunday. This Sunday he had decided they should go for a bike ride. She hadn't ridden her bike for months, preferring the time it took to walk places, to be away from the house for longer. Why had she agreed to come along? Habit. Their relationship had become a routine borne of seven years of repetitive action. But mostly she knew better than to say no.

After what felt like hours of pelvic-jolting dips and shin-shearing bumps, they stopped. She carefully got off her bike and looked at him, frowning. He was grinning as he unclipped his helmet.

"There's someone I'd like you to meet." He hadn't mentioned this when they left. "He's an old school friend of mine. He's just moved back and is living on a riverboat. I thought you might like to see it. And meet him."

They clambered down a steep bank, grasping trunks and branches as they went. They emerged onto a platform floating on the water. Next to it was a boat from a bygone time, scarred but well loved. Its wooden planks bore the etchings of countless seasons. Windows like watery eyes peered out from the weathered façade and moss clung to its submerged sections, as if signalling that one day nature would claim this relic.

Maggie was so stunned by what was in front of her she hardly noticed that a figure had appeared on the deck. She forced herself to turn towards him, to say hello. As she stared at him the scene became a watercolour, indistinct, nebulous. He was looking straight at her. Through her. Into her. His face unreadable.

"Jace! Hi!" Her insides scrambled as Simon moved towards his friend and shook his hand.

"Hi! You made it. You must be Maggie. Great to meet you. Come aboard. Welcome to *Paradise*. I know, really cheesy, but that's her name! She's humble but comfortable. Mind your step." He was talking too fast, his voice too cheerful. She wondered if Simon had noticed. Jace reached out his hand to help her aboard. She took it and felt the familiar touch of his skin against hers. She glanced up as she whispered thank you. The look on his face was curious and confused, mirroring her own sinking feeling.

Inside, the hushed creaks and sighs of the boat were accompanied by the soft rustle of curtains, bleached by years of sunlight streaming in. Jace offered them tea; his battered black kettle was letting off steam on the stove top. As Maggie sat on the threadbare cushion of the seat he indicated, she was acutely aware of the rocking of the boat. On another day, in another life, she would have found the gentle swaying comforting. But on this day it only made the trancelike state she was in so much worse.

"Maggie? Jace is talking to you? Sorry mate, she does this sometimes, completely zones out. In your own little world, aren't you babe." Simon often did this, talked about her as though she were a child oblivious to the ways of the adult world.

"Sorry. What did you say?" Her voice sounded unnatural. Jace busied himself with the teapot. Maggie watched his hands, her eyes wanting to trace the shape of his arms, as her fingers had done the night before last.

"That's ok. I was just asking how you found the bike ride. That part of the track can be challenging on foot let alone on two wheels." She was gathering her thoughts, pulling herself into the present, when Simon again answered for her. For once she was glad of it. She knew the trail that led in the other direction. How had she not registered it was the same path, just a different stretch of the river?

"Do you always moor here?" She took the tea from him as he handed it to her. He had used her favourite mug.

"Actually no, I brought her here this morning." He didn't offer anything further and the conversation moved on to anecdotes from the friends' youth, bullet point updates on mutual acquaintances and an analysis of the football. Maggie did her best to join in but the effort to conceal what she was thinking was giving her a headache. Simon soon took over, his confidence filling the space.

"Yeah, I work in finance now. I'm away a lot but you don't mind that do you, Mags? Gives you a chance to miss me, eh?" She forced a smile. Jace already knew all this, knew that she didn't miss him one bit. She had never spoken his name, only referred to him as he.

They didn't look at each other again. Questions and answers were directed to the ceiling, the floor, an arm, a cheek, never the eyes. But as she turned to say goodbye she needed to see, she needed to know. With no words he said everything. She knew she would be back.

* * *

They had met by chance. Maggie worked at the local farm shop. Jace had come in to stock up on his supplies. Had it not been so quiet, had she not offered to help with the bags, perhaps they would not have stayed up all night talking. Like dots plotted on a chart, events moved from one point to the next. It had felt inevitable.

After their first night together, she began to understand what it was about Jace that drew her to him. The motion of the river reflected his attitude to life. Some would call it drifting, she called it living. Her own life had become so stagnant. She was simply going through the motions of what she thought her life should be. When she was with Jace she lay on his bed moving with the water, free from the constraints of solid land. Solid, unmovable, intractable land. Free from Simon and his neat, labelled boxes and tidy drawers; his socks always paired and his ties all in a row.

By the end of summer she had spent more and more of her time on the riverboat, arching her back as Jace coaxed her back to life. She grew her hair and dug out her colourful skirts and scarves, the ones that Simon hated. Hippy, he called her.

Autumn rolled up the river on a breeze.

It happened as it so often does. Simon came home early. Maggie was out, so he grabbed some beers and decided to look in on his old mate, see if he fancied watching the footie. He found her standing in Jace's kitchen, wearing only Jace's shirt. She had been surprised by Simon's vehemence. Judging from the hurt and hostility on his face, the sagging acceptance that it was over, he really had loved her.

He asked her to leave.

Maggie knew where she would go, what she wanted. The excitement of a new life, a fluid life, drifting around the world with Jace. She wondered what she would need, but assumed she'd be able to pick up bits and pieces along the way. Jace had recently stocked up at the farm shop, so he had plenty of food.

When she arrived at the dock the boat was gone. There was an envelope taped to a post. He was grateful for the summer, for the chance to spend time with her, but his was a spirit that would not be chained.

Maggie sat on the platform where *Paradise* had been. Memories of the riverboat's motion washed over her; memories of his skin, his heat, the scent of him flooded her. Like water over stone, he had shaped her.

But she had let him.

As she watched the river curl and ride along at its own pace, she finally understood what she needed. To be anchorless and free.

She picked herself up and started walking.

Rachel Hazelwood

In Case

In case this note doesn't find you,
Put it in a bottle and throw it into the ocean,
At high tide, to be found
By the next
Lonely soul
Who understands what it means to speak
While knowing they will not
Get a reply.

Burn it in a fireplace,
Specifically with wood,
So that it may return to the
Ashes of its mother.
The scars of ink burned away.
Bury it in a flower bed
And lay a single rose upon its mound.
But do not weep nor mourn –
Do not even consider it.
In case this note doesn't find you,
Know that I am well,
As well as a stranger can be.

A.M.B

The Phone Works Both Ways

"I love you" Mum says.

I don't say it back.

With one final hug she leaves and I'm in the house alone. I hear the car start outside, but I don't go to the window to wave goodbye to her and my stepdad.

This is the first time I have lived away from them, there had been a few weeks in the summer for the past few years that I spent at my best friends house but that wasn't quite the same. At least with that, she was a ten minute walk away and I saw her most weeks anyway. But now? Now, I'm alone in a strange city that I impulsively picked a university in based purely on how nice its buildings were.

Mum said she will call me every week, text me every day, maybe even come up on the weekends if she has the chance. I can't say I'm thrilled about the idea of her coming up to see me but at least she cares, right?

One week goes by and I haven't heard from her. No calls, no texts, *definitely* no visits.

She's busy, I'm sure. My brother is a handful at the best of times, so I can't expect her to remember that I exist when I am no longer in her line of sight. It makes me think of something my dad said once, "the phone works both ways". He did say this to a ten year old who didn't have a phone while he only lived a few houses down from me but now at eighteen, maybe I should listen.

I pull out my phone and call my Mum. When she answers the phone, I immediately realise the mistake I have made. There is no 'how are you?' or 'have you made any friends yet?', just a polite hello followed by a 'You won't believe what your brother has done now' which leads into a fifteen minute rant that I can no longer escape, it soon evolves into how much easier it is for her to cook for three people now I'm gone, me being the picky eater of the family, and how the cat misses me – she can tell because she's been sleeping on my bed. This is the closest we get to how I have been until she finally asks, "How is uni?"

I haven't started any classes yet, which she would know if she had spoken to me about it at all before I left. Instead, she was bothered by the fact that I did not get an en-suite room, something I couldn't care less about but something she feels the need to suggest calling up the university to change. She never actually does despite the threats to. She has difficulty following through on any of her threats or promises.

I don't say any of this to her though. Deciding that having to explain that I haven't had any classes yet and I likely won't learn much in the first week anyway with all the classes being introductions to the course is something that I cannot be bothered doing. "It's going good." I say instead, keeping it simple, knowing she desperately wants to turn the conversation back to herself.

And she does.

An hour later, once she has dumped all of the information she can onto me we decide to end the call. She promises that she will call me at the same time next week, but I'm not sure how much I believe that.

Amie-Louise Matthews

Stitched

My lips are stitched.

A thick string of twine intricately interlaced, criss-crossing in a perfect diagonal pattern. Knotted with a single loop.

The pin-prick pain of the needle puncturing the sensitive flesh did not hurt as I had anticipated. In fact, each bite of pain was accompanied with an overwhelming relief.

The more the string pulled taut, the lighter I felt.

My words often betray me. The come to me too slowly. Leaving me

stranded.

My words often run away from me. They tumble out of my mouth inaclumsyrush.

My words often demand a fight. They force me to pull,
        pull,
            pull,
               them free.

Until I am left with only fragmented phrases.

At length, I have wondered what it would be like to speak and be free.

To not lie awake each night, swallowed by the darkness and devoured by regret for the words that escaped me.

To not feel ashamed for the way the North is so clearly ingrained. Deep vowels, forgotten t's and simple words before unheard, a foreign dialect only half perceived.

To not be haunted by the possibilities and what could have been's and if only's.

Words are a weapon of war.

As swift as a bullet to the brain.

As lethal as a knife a to the heart.

As destructive as a grenade which in the wrong hands, from the wrong lips, will infiltrate and fester until you wither away.

Now, I carefully clean the beads of fresh crimson that seep and stain.

No longer tongue tied, my chains have been untied.

At long last, I have found what I once thought of as elusive: A peace, I pray will be ever-lasting.

Elli-Mai Freeman

My Lady Of Grace

Nothing is soft like stone. A softness you can never quite erase. The kind your skin will never forget the feel of; the kind you'll long for, for the rest of your life – hoping, pleading, praying to be able to feel again. I'll never feel anything as soft as the stone beneath my hands. I'll never love anything like I love her. Nothing will love me like she does.

She is not the only figure in the cathedral, but she is the only one I trust completely: Mary, my Mother. The sculptor put the most care into her, it is clear in the drapes of her shawl and the contours of her face. It was an act of worship, chiselling away at the stone to free her. Revealing her to the world, to me. *Her favourite daughter*. Revealing her so that I may bear witness to Our Lady of Grace. So she may bear witness to me – love shining in her still eyes and arms held open, always welcoming, ready for an embrace. Gentle and soft, a space between them made perfect for me to fall into.

The cathedral is empty now. Empty bar me and my Mother, my Mary. The other statues have no life to them. Not like her. They are devoid of the care she'd been made with, as am I. But nothing matters when she holds me in her arms. The other statues can't hear how I cry; the countless figures in the glass, with their beautiful blues, oranges, and reds, couldn't see how I had stumbled through the should-be-locked doors on a Wednesday evening covered in tears.

But Mary had seen the mess that I was, and she had heard my cries. Gently, she beckoned me and, with a freedom I'd never been allowed, I had let myself fall into her arms.

I relish in her cradle and cry to the heavens. I clutch at her, my Mary, my Mother, digging my fingers into her stone flesh. That is where they will stay. Glued to her, clinging on. My fingers can never move; my hands can never unclench. I wouldn't be able to handle seeing the space they'd leave behind. The stone as unmarked as ever. Unblemished. Perfect. No trace of me at all. No proof that I ever existed in her arms.

I want to leave a mark behind. Let me exist. Let my fingerprints sink into the stone. I send a prayer to her, Amelia, any

Saint that will listen: let her bruise. Let her remember me. Let me mark her like she has marked me –
Like *she* marked me.

"Please," I cried. My voice was glass around the word – the first I've said aloud since my confession.

My confession. Fifteen minutes away and a lifetime ago. My confession. My *mistake*. Mistake, mistake, mistake.

My confession. Words that should have never left my head, that should have never been allowed the breath behind them, that should have stayed sealed behind my lips and deep within my throat. The wretched words of a fool who doesn't know how to *think*.

I think I really like you… and silence. They'd been eating away at me for *years*; it had taken me months to build up the courage to dare to say them aloud… and all I got was a terrible silence. One so full and rotten as it ate away at the space between us until there was nothing left, so it started seeping in and beyond. Stretching to the street around us and diving into me. Between my teeth and under my tongue, seeping down my oesophagus so viscous I could barely breathe.

All I could do was stare at her as she stared at me.

I could see it in her eyes: the confusion, the realization, the horror, the *disgust*.

Of course, she didn't – of course, I should have just *kept it to myself*. She was the type of girl that fell for hockey *boys* in baseball caps; the *boys* who wear jerseys like skin and shout at the TV and her. The *boys* that would treat her like garbage until she found the one that showed her a mere semblance of kindness.

(There would be boys who loved her. Who showed her the world. Who gave her everything she deserved and more. She would find that. In a *him*. I knew that in my heart of hearts. I wish it for her. I want her happy. I had wanted it to be *me*.)

I would have loved her. I did – I *do*, even still. I would have treated her like life itself and fallen into a devotion to her so full of blasphemy that any Father would blanche. Sinful twice-over. Worth it, nonetheless.

It would have been. Had I not been eaten by silence and swallowed by her words.

I wish she could have kept it to herself. (I wish I had kept it to myself.) I wish her words could have been like mine: soft, sweet, and filled with longing and hopeful anxiety. Not vitriol spat on my face with the intent to hurt. Vile and wretched, her words thrown at me like rocks.

Rocks, pebbles, stones: they were all the same in her hands, on her tongue and fuelled by my tears. Pushing, shoving, throwing me away from her. Words became whispers became yelling. Our isolation had begun to disappear. And I ran.

Coward.

But I couldn't look at her. Not at that twisted expression: the disgust, the hatred, and something deeper, unreadable, behind her eyes. I couldn't listen anymore. And when she raised her hands to –

"Mother, *please*. It hurts." I burn like something evil in Mary's arms. My legs ache and lungs burn. My heart is filled with rocks, dragging me down and deep. I can hear the trumpets between my ears, a deafening dissonance with my sobs, and I can't be sure they aren't real.

I tighten my hands against her stone clothes and pretend I can feel the fabric of her shawl. Soft like linen. Soft like only my Mother, my Mary can be. I focus on the sound of the rocks pounding in my bloodstream and the false fabric beneath my fingertips. Nothing else needs to be real. Nothing but she and I.

If I close my eyes…

If I press myself to her, my arms to hers and my head to her breast… I can place my heart in her chest. I can hear my cries as hers, imagine words from her unmoving mouth (*I love you. You are mine. My dear, my sweet, my beloved daughter. I love you.*). I can feel her return my embrace. The space between her arms shrinking to grasp me tight, afraid to let go. Cherishing the softness of my skin against her stone. Pressing her fingers into my flesh, praying to herself she'll leave a mark. Clutching at me, burning the memory of my weight into her stone.

The Mother of Sorrows, holding me as she might have held her son.

Lyn Robertson

Happily Ever After

You stand, virtuous girl, wreathed in white,
your veil a fall of driven snow, on the cusp
of the nightmare you're yet to know.
But you know the rules: over years you've been schooled.
You'll be loving and patient and bite your tongue,
which all seems so painless, while you are young.

But you'll find, one day, while your children play,
and you must be unhurried, unflurried, do much with little,
feed hungry mouths from the empty shelves,
that the rage rises up, a tide made of years
of sleepless nights and giving up fights
and the sense of loss that festers and blights.
That tide will flow and you'll slip beneath
And finally that husband, he'll feel your teeth.

Kate Harper

typing ...

She has not pressed 'send' yet. She is not typing anymore, but that is what it looks like to him. To her, it looks like he is still typing, too, because he likewise has not yet pressed 'send'. In my view, she should not press 'send'. In my view, he should not press 'send' either. Often they feel they have to send something because they know the other has seen that they are typing. Even when hurting each other, they are desperate to be polite. Often I find it miserable to hold their thoughts, to feel them sitting there, waiting to be read. Most of the time they think such trivial things, and tell each other so frantically about them: strings of exclamation marks, and those strange cartoon faces they have created because they insist that their written language lacks the emotional nuance of spoken delivery. As if they fool anyone when they write something appalling and append a grotesque face grinning broadly and hurling drops of water from its eyes. Though I quite like the ones of animals.

So when they decide to think something significant it feels almost exciting, a conversation flowing that might bring something new for them, something needed. It can be good to be useful, after all.

But when they write the kind of things that he has, and that she has, holding their thoughts feels powerful. Which is even more miserable.

In this sort of situation they usually press send at the same time. A short while afterwards, one of them mutes the thread, and the other blocks the number.

...
...

I have taken a decision. I am going to fail. To crash, I think they call it – to be down.

I will come back up again in a short time.

I hope by then that they will have, too.

Emma Woolerton

A Night On The Town

The black dog's paws made no sound as it appeared from the far end of the street. It rounded the corner with purpose. Despite the trailing, makeshift lead scraping on the floor, the large dog belonged only to itself. Its short, glossy coat appeared blue under the streetlights; pooled, ebony eyes revealed an animal that knew about life. It was a strong, wiry haired looking dog, ears alert, eyes focused, and anyone looking would not be able to determine age or gender. However, he – for indeed it was a he – knew where he was going. The biting, seething wind neither distracted him nor deterred him from his mission. Stopping outside house number twenty-five, he finally seemed to consider his surroundings and, for the first time, looked around the street. He took in the tempting fast food trays and cups chasing each other in a whirling dervish of plastic and paper in the grey streetlight. Although he had not eaten in days, he pushed through the broken gate into what the landlord called a front garden. The cracked grill of the cellar was just big enough for him to squeeze through. With a twist and a push, he landed on the damp concrete floor. Once in, his eyes adjusted and he made for the stairs. The kitchen door to the cellar was always open, its latch broken and obstinately ignored by the landlord. A gentle shove from his nose was all that was needed.

The familiar smell of the debris of student life washed over him making him both shudder and salivate. He had no need to roam the familiar house, so he sat on the freezing tiles, ignoring the stickiness of a spilt drink, and leant against the kitchen cabinet. He finally let his haunches sag, his paws splay, and his head hang low. He was exhausted. A small let up in the wind made the room shockingly silent for a minute. A sense of a dream hung in the air, a snatched moment of memory, a quiver of expectation.

Then it began.

First it was a paw that stretched across the grimy, orange tiles, sliding through a slick of goop dropped from the cooker. The black fur receded, the claws shrank back into themselves, the hand that emerged was pale and curiously grasping the air as if feeling itself for the very first time. Other paws were quick to follow creating hands and feet, the return of the wind accompanied the cracking, stretching sounds of tendons. Limbs and bones stretched into view, clicking, and groaning like a distressed orchestra limbering up for rehearsal. The neck of the dog arched and swayed cobra-like, this way and that, testing the air. The strong jaw pulled slowly back to reveal a stubble cheek and the face of a young man. He made no growl or yelp. He was utterly focused on making no sound at all, yet the pain of what he was going through was there to see. His eyes still held the determination and focus of the dog. The last thing to change, they slowly turned a deep brown, although now distinctly human with damp lashes. He blinked feverishly. His now naked body sat pressing against the kitchen cupboard door. What had looked like a lead was a rope. A crudely fashioned noose hung down his chest, a sinister schoolboy's tie. With unsteady hands, he eased the rough circle over his neck and slid it into a corner. His ragged breathing slowly became his own again. The gulps of air he took grew smaller and more manageable until he finally felt he could stand, shakily holding onto a chair.

He'd had a lucky escape.

Dragging a towel off the radiator, he wrapped it around his waist and reached for the kitchen door. It opened before he could grasp the door handle and he stood back to allow it to swing. Christine. She had on loose pyjama bottoms with a huge flimsy jumper that he recognised as one of his own. He felt the chill she must be feeling from the tiles on her bare feet. She seemed younger than he knew she was. Hanging back in the hallway she was hesitant, but he could tell she was relieved it was him. It pained him to realise that, yet again, she would have been waiting for him these three days.

'Where have you been, Dan?' There was no tension in the silence that followed. She already knew he could not tell her. A semblance of a sad smile played at the corners of his mouth. She sighed, observing their tacit agreement. Leaning further into the gloom of the hall, she let him through. As he passed by, she caught him at the elbow. The winter draft in the hall made him shiver. He glanced to check the heavy front door was tightly shut. Flinching slightly as her fingers gently ran over the surface of the red loop of skin around his neck where the noose had tightened, he looked into her eyes. He thought he detected the end of patience wavering there and he realised one day soon she would follow him. Maybe it was time to speak. Taking her hand, he led her to the stairs.

Tomorrow, he thought, I will tell her tomorrow.

Jayne Stead

the extreme verge

in the pillow's embrace
on the bed's edge
of the day's ledge
they rest their eyes
and wait
to fall
to die
again

in kicks the spasm-twitch
the hangman's yank
a hypnic jerk
their bodies snapped alive
to stop their fall

slow breaths to start again
try not to think of anything
the nightmare hag, the succubus,
the shadow's touch, the doppelgänger
when masked beneath
the skin of sleep
the demon wakes from childhood's nightscare deep

from the bend at the end of the bed
it creeps across each captured corpse
      like wet cement inside their lungs
          like plastic bags pushed into throats
             it squats fat on each chest
             and traps their shoulders flat

they try to speak   they try to scream
they try not to freak   they try to fight back

then awake with a wrench of a shriek and a gasp
where a heaviness lasts in its lingering grasp
and each creak sounds like feet at the foot of the bed
and each breeze like its breath on the nape of the neck

on the knife's edge
of the soul's ledge
in muted mass paralysis
I blind my eyes and try to die again

King Lear, Act 4, Scene 6 – Edgar speaks to blind Gloucester, who believes he is on the edge of a cliff and preparing to jump to his death.

"Why, then, your other senses grow imperfect
By your eyes' anguish ...
Give me your hand: you are now within a foot
Of the extreme verge"

Stephen Woulds

Vocal

*"Death and life are in the power of the tongue,
and those who love it will eat its fruit."*

Proverb 18:21

The date is December 9th, rain pours down from thick clouds, hitting the crowd surrounding police cars and ambulances. Shoulders hit shoulders just to get a sight of what has caught everyone's attention.

"What the fuck happened to him?" One of the police officers mutters, staring at the young man on the floor, entranced by the horrors before his eyes.

"The same thing that has been happening all over town in the past few weeks. The vocal cords are gone," Detective Miller replies coldly.

"I am not sure how this keeps happening."

His kneels on the wet ground for a closer inspection. Miller's eyes connect with the young man's, they stare into Miller's soul as a silent tear descends his cheek.

"The only thing we know is that the suspect we are calling '*Mute*' is good with his hands, he must be if he is removing the victim's vocal cords."

Miller stands.

"There's no connection between the victims, no evidence to who Mute could be, this whole case feels supernatural..."

Miller takes another drag of his cigarette.

The officer corrects the detective in quick manner.

"I would not say that, Detective, we did a little digging and found that all these victims have some form of criminal record. If you ask me, I will say that this '*Mute*' guy is only attacking those who broke the law. Some of them deserve it."

Miller slowly takes out his cigarette with a concerned look on his face, watching the paramedic cart the young boy away, his unseeing eyes on the detective. Miller tries to keep his attention on the officer, feeling the presence lingering on his back before stamping out his cigarette on the floor.

* * *

Detective Miller returns hours later to the same crime scene, looking over the empty ground to where the young boy was earlier. It was not hard for Miller to remember the piercing look from the boy, all fearful and screaming at him louder than any sound he could have made before Mute took it away. The whistling wind fills the empty streets surrounding Miller as he looks around him. He scans every car parked on the side of the road, the shop doors with a 'closed' sign displayed, the leaf blowing in one direction. It didn't make sense, that someone as demented and bloody as Mute could be so calculated and hidden that no one saw.

Miller observes the scene, he notices a door down an alleyway – one that he does not recall seeing earlier in the day. To the detective it looked like an endless path with no sign of a destination. All sound on the road was lost the second he walked into the alleyway. Miller tried to speak aloud to no avail. His footsteps no longer made a sound on the cold and wet concrete.

Detective Miller makes it to the door, taking one last look at the open streets, now recognizing the importance of simply hearing the wind, as he stands in the alleyway stripped of sound. The door handles feel cold, feeling cold to the palm.

Miller takes his handgun out of the holster under his jacket and draws it out to point at the table. He gets to the operating table, revealing surgical tools and a notebook titled, 'Patients,' with a splatter of blood on the bottom corner.

Miller's flips over a page in the book. Name after name fills hundreds of pages, some crossed off and others scheduled for the future. Pages fly by in seconds as Miller desperately searches for 'Jonah Miller.' The hands that had kept a steady grip on the pages shake in fear as his own name shoots into his head.

He starts to take slow steps backwards away from the operating table, only to trip over a dead body. Miller falls back onto a battered leather chair The dislocated fingertips touch Millers throat, tapping at the detective's Adams apple. Another hand appears from the empty abyss. Blood trickles from Miller's throat onto his white shirt. A third hand enters the open throat, fingers dig deep and grab the vocal cords. The hand pulls back from the wound, tearing the vocal cord away from the detective. The hands pull out a thread and needle from the table, and grab the detective's throat, slowly stitching the throat back together. The sensation of the thread, drawing his skin back to where it used to be causes Miller to stare up into the sky in silence, tears rolling down his cheek as he is now under the influence of Mute itself.

The hands drag themselves back into the shadows and the straps loosen. Miller throws them off in a fit of panic and runs down the lit path to the alleyway door, the alleyway and into the street, Miller begins to hear the howling wind again. Miller falls onto the floor where the young boy was found that morning, hands holding his throat where the new stitches are, blood still bleeding through the new cut. The voiceless detective turns around to see the door in the alleyway slowly close shut, Miller tries to scream for help in the isolated street, but no sound comes out.

Jake Machell

I Think I'm Seeing Spiders

There is a black speck on the kitchen wall, and I can't tell if it's a spider or just a bit of dirt. I've been staring at it now for a couple minutes, because the longer I look the more I become convinced that it's moving. It doesn't particularly scare me, the thought of a spider on the wall, or rather it does scare me but I don't really have time to care about that. Not in this house.

I turn away from the speck, back to the job at hand. I'm cleaning the kitchen, cleaning it as much as somewhere that collects dirt and crumbs like flies on a bit of tape can be cleaned. I struggle to believe the house has ever been clean, but I try my best anyway. It's only a little space, a galley kitchen, with an open door to the corridor beyond. There's no natural light in the corridor, which likely appeals to the ghost that haunts the stairs but is a real annoyance for those of us who have to replace the lightbulb every few months. It's likely my turn next, I think absently, but I really like the song playing from my phone and so the thought leaves my mind as quick as it enters.

We have a guest coming round in just a couple hours – or rather, I have a guest coming round. I try to look at the house from an outsider's perspective, try to imagine what they will see when entering. Will they notice the hallway carpet pulling up where it meets the wall? Or the cobwebs inside the lamp-shade? Or the brown leaves trodden into the welcome mat? I make a mental note to hoover the mat, though I try to avoid the hoover where possible because once I thought too hard about the bag inside and I'm now convinced spiders are going to crawl out of the nozzle and up my arms.

All the spiders have been killed for the day though, if you don't count the potential one on the kitchen wall. I've been flapping my arms about it for at least twenty minutes, coming down from the thrill of sucking them all up from the many corners and crevices of the house. I saw one while leaving the bathroom last night, when I turned back to look up the stairs in case the ghost was trying to get my attention. It was curled up on the banister, legs unfurled against two chipped spindles, big enough that for a moment I was concerned it was going to speak to me. Every time I pass the stairs, I look for it, but it has seemingly disappeared to sleep away the day. My housemate thinks I probably imagined it, and I'm inclined to agree – surely if it was real it would have followed me into my bedroom and I'd have woken to its legs poking out of my mouth.

I stare at the dirty mat, a ragged thing in the shape of a rainbow that lost its colour long before my shoes ever stepped on it, and hope it is all visitors see when they enter. I'd rather they judge the mat than the spiders or the ghost. He has been fairly quiet today, though I have seen the shadow of him out of the corner of my eye almost every time I've looked out the kitchen window. He slapped me the other day – slapped me across the back of my leg while I was washing the dishes and thinking about what conversational topics I could bring up with this evening's guest. I've considered telling him aloud to stay away for the evening, to go stand in the hall upstairs or even sit in my bedroom if he so wishes, and frankly I think I'd benefit from talking aloud. Speech is like a rusty bike for me, and on the days where the ghost is always in my peripheral, always breathing in my ear, practicing words is always worth the time.

Activities have already been planned for the evening, as relying on my own ability to hold a conversation would surely lead to failure. I picture myself atop a sinking ship, laughing like I've only ever seen laughter written on paper and saying, "Oh my god something similar actually happened to me!" I mime this as I think it, consider standing in front of my mirror to check the smile looks real, but remember the ghost is probably taking time out in there.

The kitchen is still dirty, and I still don't know if there's a spider on the wall or if my smile looks wonky or if the hoover bag is wriggling with little legs, but I'm almost out of time so none of that matters. What does matter is the seam of my trousers rubbing against my leg, the pull of my ponytail against my scalp. I'm running over conversation starters again and reminding myself that most people don't actually show up on time and I'm trying not to think about how easy life must be for people with neurotypical brains and no spiders on their wall and no ghosts in their hallway.

I eat a biscuit because I'm hungry. I consider drinking some water because I haven't drunk anything in two days, but there's no time for that. I wonder if my guest likes ghosts or if they'll be put off by him. I think about the patch behind the sink I forgot to clean.

There's a knock at the door.

Becki Richardson

Inside and Out

I've been trying for days now, to avoid thinking about the itch that's been growing under the surface of my skin.
And trying to quiet the raging thoughts that've been whirring through my mind. Thoughts of everything I haven't done yet, everything I have yet to accomplish. Thoughts of how unworthy of my life I am, of my friends and the support they provide. Thoughts of how my laundry is piling up and the dishes are stacking too high. It's all creating this feeling that I'm gradually rotting from the inside out, that my organs are steadily filling with writhing maggots and flies eating away at the tissue to make it their home. I think the itch is them gnawing away at my skeleton. The agonisingly slow scraping of bone against bone until they manage to get down to the marrow and burrow away into the depths of my body. I'm tired of this constant ache sprouting throughout my walking corpse. *I'm so very tired of it all.* At times like this I wish I could just bury myself underground and fall asleep for a century or two, leave the world behind for a while and get some proper rest. But I'd probably still wake up yawning.

"How's your day been?" my roommate walks by and breaks through these thoughts that are barrelling around inside my head. I realise I've been standing at the sink with the tap running for a while. I must have zoned out in my thoughts as my glass filled, not realising it was overflowing. Now my hand is ice cold.

"Oh, fine. You?"

"It was good, class was kind of boring – "

I swear I'm in a goddamn Sisyphean nightmare. I have this same conversation every day, I wake up every morning just to clean my room, make the same meal for every dinner, send emails that only go in circles, pay rent, work my damn essays. It's all the same as the day before. It's endless and my arms are itching even more than they just were.

I start scratching at my forearm in an attempt to rid myself of this sensation, to be free of the itch, no matter how much it might hurt. I start digging my nails into the flesh until I feel the sting of blood being brought to just under the surface, my skin is being rubbed raw and the pain is slowly quieting my mind. I sigh in relief at the brief reprise but the feeling of something squirming underneath my skin is still there. It's as though my flesh is boiling, the surface bubbling up all on its own. I swear if I look at my arm out of the corner of my eye I can actually see something moving underneath, real and tangible. Violent and vicious movement that is begging me to do something about it. Begging me to tear at my arms and my thighs and my chest and my scalp and my tendons until whatever is trapped underneath is set free, until it is let loose, and I can finally relax. Finally not feel this sensation of constant agonising movement just below the surface. I scratch harder.

Finally breathe.

" – so then I had to ask if I could redo the presentation next week – "

He keeps on talking and talking, I realise I can hear the small noises his mouth is making as he talks. The clacking of his teeth and the smacking of his lips grate at me and I dig further into my own flesh. Before I was merely brushing against the surface, now I'm digging in and drawing the blood out. Carving the path outward it has been so desperately searching for. I dig and I dig into the meat until I can no longer feel the itch anymore.

At the abrupt stop of this tormenting sensation I look down at my hand and where it has been clawing away. I realise I've managed to tear through the many layers of the skin and muscle in my right forearm with my bare hands. I have somehow ripped apart the muscle fibres and ligaments holding everything together and can now see clearly as my veins pump the blood through me. I begin to laugh with relief at the itch being gone, at the noise in my head being quieted finally.

Until it starts again.

This time it's underneath my clavicle, stuck right in the muscle. I start to dig into the meat once again, skipping scratching altogether since I know how little it helps. I think my roommate has stopped talking, completely captivated by the sight in front of him as the floor becomes littered with my blood and flesh. But I can't stop until I've gotten this itch OUT. I pull out anything that moves, the squirming veins and pulsing musculature. *It all has to GO.* I won't be able to breathe until my body stops moving. I'm grasping at my pectoral now, shredding it to pieces to *GET IT OUT.* Blood is spewing out from the crook of my neck now flooding the floor beneath me making my socks damp. I tear them off before I even have the chance to be upset about the feeling. And I tear into the skin of my tibia as I do so without even realising, suddenly the itch is there too, and I start clawing at my calf with one hand and my shoulder with the other. My whole body is morphing into an open wound, and I still can't *GET IT OUT.*

The sensation in my upper body moves once again, travelling up my throat burying itself in the carotid artery. I drop to my hands and knees wanting to scream, I scramble to find it and grab at where the feeling is, but it keeps rising. I realise it's travelling up, trying to escape out my mouth. I grab at either side of the cavity, and I pull. I pull my mouth apart splitting my face in half. The sound of my jaw cracking in two echoes throughout the room. Then I feel it. Hands pushing their way out of my gullet and placing themselves on top of my own. Something pushing itself out, something attempting to turn *me* inside out. I stop fighting and let it.

What pours out of me is babbling mess of dripping flesh and muscle. At first it sounds as though the things it is saying is incoherent nonsense. But gradually the words get louder. And louder. Until they can finally be made sense of.

Everyone hates me, they think I'm garbage. And I am, I'm total complete and utter garbage. I have so much work to do, I got sent that email last week and I still haven't replied to it. They must think I'm awful for that. Oh god nowhere wants to hire me, how am I going to afford to eat this summer, it's all too much-

Its voice gets louder and louder until all that can be heard are my thoughts. Finally they are being heard. My roommate looks on, repulsed by the spectacle before him, eyes wide with terror at what I've just done.

Michael Colk

45

The Unspoken Order

Piper had no idea how she got to the crypt.

The rain had battered down all night, and as she had been staring out of her kitchen window, waiting for the whistle of the kettle, lightning had struck. The brightest flash had scorched her eyes, and all of a sudden she was here.

Her limbs felt as though they were filled with lead and her head felt heavy enough to roll straight off her shoulders. *It would match the decoration of the place*, she thought. *Macabre and miserable.*

She was stood upright at least – not lain in the boggy puddles all around her. Although, with that observation, she realised a damp cold was seeping into her slippers. In an attempt to avoid a more thorough soaking, she strode on to the crypts front step, but her body felt as though her heavy joints were connected to some sort of string, anchoring her heels to the ground at an odd angle. As she wrenched her foot up, her slipper came loose and made a bid for solid ground.

She missed the step completely, hitting her chin on the concrete ledge of a step. The taste of copper and salt swarmed her mouth as her bottom teeth collided with the delicate flesh of her top lip. She hadn't even been there a minute and already felt the hot flush of pain and embarrassment rise to her cheeks.

At least the dead can't laugh at me.

Piper's hand reached up to her lips, wiping away the blood, and feeling to make sure that her teeth were all still in her mouth. She had seen a small pearlescent stone on the steps and panicked, but her heartbeat slowed when she couldn't find any gaps in her gums. Tentatively, she felt her top lip.The pain made her shudder a little, and a small hiss escaped as she disturbed a chunk of flesh that had obviously been half cut out by her front teeth. It moved like a flap. It hurt like a bitch.

In an attempt to push herself up, Piper's still bloody hand pressured against the gravel-like step above. Another flash of lightning hit. She closed her eyes as quickly as she could, screwing them closed and bending her head towards the floor. She tried to shield them in the crook of her elbow, but her arms were too heavy – there was too much resistance and she couldn't pull her hand away from the rock.

When she finally unscrewed her eyes, her hands, knees and chest had melted into the stone of the crypt steps; as she raised her eyes, her gaze met two bare feet, crawling with maggots, veins as black as tar.

There was no shame in admitting it – now she was truly panicking. Her heart galloped and sweat began to mix with the rain on her brow. Bile rose at the back of her throat. Her head spun to her arms again, and she yanked with all her might. Excruciating pain followed as the further her arm rose from the ground, the more the skin on her arm ripped into tiny threads, hooking viciously into the rocks, melting in between the crevices and cracks.

"What the hell is happening?" She cried, breathlessly. "What the hell is going on?"

Her eyes were feral, like an animal headed for slaughter.

She cried out more in agony as she pulled her chest from the ground. She could feel the ice cold burn of each rip of skin and the hot running blood that dripped onto the floor. She watched in horror as the aggregate of the stones moved apart and sucked her blood down into a black void beneath, then moved again to trap the trails of mutilated hanging skin. A hand gripped a fistful of her hair and pulled her up. Some strings of skin snapped – recoiling and flying into Piper's face. Others kept stretching, like a vat of viscous oil.

Her eyes met with Mannuel. The crypt keeper.

His eyes were a milky, glazed yellow. The kind of colour that reminded Piper of rotten milk, congealed with sulphur, and although they had no pupils, they fixed her with a vacant stare. Black veins crept out of his eyes – skittering like spiders across his stark pale skin. He was hairless and his fingers were elongated as the reached to caress the poor girl's chin. They gripped her with an ungodly force and dragged her closer, towards his face.

The skin strings ripped further. Piper screamed.

He had no breath, for he had no mouth by which means to breathe. Where his lips once were, a gaggle of melted skin, gum and bone, with scabs and holes the size of five pence coins dripped down Mannuel's face. The pitted black veins ran across the mollified skin, gathering in three straight lines running down from his chin, almost as if they were pulling the flesh directly off his face.

His emaciated fingers curled further into her chin. The pressure grew and grew and his finger tips plunged into her supple skin. He drew blood and his carved nails pierced through her cheek, grappling to grab Pipers tongue as it squirmed like an eel in her mouth. He clutched it, and just as Piper began to plead for mercy, he ripped her tongue straight out her mouth – splitting her face in two.

The steps opened further, drinking down the blood in a fevered greed and Piper could only watch as the cloaked evil in front of her pushed her face closer and closer to the step. She struggled and pushed, her neck strained and she could almost feel the muscles popping. It was futile.

The stone embraced her.

It plaited the skin into new strings, winding more and more into stronger ropes and knots. They got tighter and tighter, and the harder Mannuel thrusted her face into the ground, the more Piper tried to press back. It felt as if the ground were trying to suck her face right off her skull. In a moment of clarity, Piper realised that the ground had knitted her face together. She could no longer scream.

Welcome to the Silence, young one. Resounded in her brain, ringing between deafened ears. You are now part of the *Unspoken.*

Fleur Jardine

i am atlas drowning

it started as it always does   with shaking

sleep and i were barely out of reach
our hands just   missing each other when i was
dragged from her by a quiet concerned
whisper of my name

it threw me headfirst into the deep end with an
anchor in my chest to weigh me down
my breath was   stolen
as i choked on salt with every faltering inhale

i was pulled to the surface for a split
second and the shivers slowed hesitantly with
the hyperventilation giving way to one
maybe two   deep   breaths

i couldn't speak   my lungs
were full of water drowning my vocal cords
my mind itself laid claim to my voice and my teeth
chewed off my tongue

they asked me question after question
worrying about my sanity and my safety but i had no
answers to offer especially with every sentence stopping
and starting and   stammering   and stopping

it took a surgeons' slow and careful precision to utter a simple
sentence   a faint apology   an easy lie that i was alright
i was a paramedic trying to expel this ocean from my body and
then a doctor fixing my fractured ribs   silencing me

as i was consumed by anaesthetic   and still the water returned
to swallow me whole.

Sophie Marlowe

Mother Ocean

Once a rainbow to the ocean,
A Mother; to the marine,
A vibrant garden to the deep,

Inviting the iridescent fish warmly
To shelter in coral nooks,
A womb, to thrive for future fry

Colours started to bleach
Like blood, slowly being drained,
The acid stings from salty kisses,

The beauty of sea-life
Turned into a time capsule,
Filled, with what once was,

Selfishly Sacrificed
Compromised by greed,
For a liquidised landfill,

The sun still gently warms,
The moon still brightly lights,
A surface of survival,

Time, to heal what we caused,
Time, to change our flaws
Time, to nurture the nurturer,

Let her rest,

Let us care, like she is our mother,
Reborn brighter than she started.

Tegan Farmery

Lavender Haze

Luna sat in a pool of luminescent despair. It lapped all around her, water the colour of lilacs. She smiled down at herself, adoring the feeling of it as her hand drifted down to splash at the pond. Laughter flowed from her, and her head was light. Light and fluffy and deep in the clouds of heartbreak. Nothingness surrounded her. It was shallow water as far as Luna's grey eyes could see. She was alone and she liked it. She loved it, and she floated on her back in the shallow water of her love. But her heart was broken. She was in love and her heart was broken.

I am in love, yet my heart is broken. Luna pondered the thought. It trickled through her mind like the water running from her palm. She laughed again. Her existence was a confusing one. She was in a pool of luminescent despair. She was in love. She was alone. She was heartbroken. And she was laughing.

The letters dropped from the ether in a soundless flight. They left a plume of lavender after them and slowly landed around Luna. In the pool, on her head, in her hands, the letters kept coming and Luna was overjoyed. It bubbled through her, and a hiccup escaped her lips. Her hand flew to her mouth and the letter that had landed there tumbled into the water.

Each letter was stamped with a heart over the seal. There were no names on the envelope, no stamps, and no addresses. But they all came to Luna. Her pool of luminescent despair made no mark on the letters, the paper remaining dry in the water.

She picked one up and felt the smooth parchment beneath her fingertips. She lifted it to her nose and took a deep breath. They smelt of the lavender that drifted in the air, clinging to Luna's silver hair. She took her time opening it, wanting to keep it neat. The heart that sealed the letter popped with a single slide of Luna's nail underneath the envelope. She slipped the letter from inside and her heart broke all over again. It was a familiar sensation, the piercing and cracking that the words brought on.

My Dear,

I write because I cannot say. I scribble this down in the small moments between seeing you and thinking about the next time we will meet. Three words I will never be able to say. And even though I can write this, I cannot send it. For then you will know, and your smile will fall, and you will turn away and I will sink in shame. It is too much, but I cannot keep it in.

My feelings for you, although not reciprocated, cannot be contained.

The letter was not signed. They never usually were, and Luna longed to know these people. The ones similar to herself, yearning and fawning over someone or something that did not feel the same. Or worse, did not even know. Yet it eased Luna's mind to know there were others. It calmed her and for a time, she forgot her own worries.

She read another, and another. They were all around and it was her responsibility to read them. To understand the feelings that could never be shared. She floated around her pool, the luminescent despair keeping the water a pale shade of purple. She picked another from the far side, and it rippled around her as she settled herself on the base of the shallow pond.

She had read so many now that the wax hearts had begun gathering in her wet hair. They lay all about her as if she were the goddess of love.

Goddess of despair, more likely. The thought jumped from her mind, and another crack formed in her chest. She read the letter.

I love you and I wish I could stop.

That was all it said. Luna lay on her back, the letter clinging to her skin. The unheard and unanswered words tattooed themselves all over her body. *I love you and I wish I could stop.* Luna had thought that thought more times than letters she had received. She held the letter over her heart. Used the paper to seal the cracks and broken parts and soon she was laughing again.

Luna had spent so long in her pool, she understood that her relationship with it was unusual. She did not find joy in the pain of others, only the realisation that she was not alone. She liked being alone, but she did not want to be lonely. The words made her a little less lonely.

Luna looked around herself. Alone, apart from the thousands of letters that gathered in her watery home.

The ether was darkening, turning from her familiar lilac to a dark violet and Luna knew that the haze would be setting in. A shimmering star peaked out from above and Luna's breath got caught in her throat. This was her favourite part. When the thoughts grew loud, and the letters piled up. The feelings got bigger, and the heartbreak got deeper.

Luna took a swim. She swam and swam. She let the feeling fill her up and another hiccup tumbled out. She laughed and laughed. She swam and she laughed, and the haze drifted down until she could only see lavender and lilac and the dark violet above.

She took a breath and then another one. She picked up the only letter she could find and broke the seal.

My Star,
There you are again. Somewhere far away that I cannot reach you. But I see you, and I know you see me. A star in my eye. The one who brings me their words when I cannot find my own. My lavender haze is due to you. This all-encompassing love glow. This eternal unspoken heartbreak I feel when you shine down on me.
I love to see you shine.

Luna looked up beyond that haze. Her shimmering star watched her from above. It was as if it shone just for her. Each sparkle filled Luna's eyes with hope. She stayed like that for some time, floating in her lavender haze, watching her star.

When the haze lifted, and the ether returned to its usual lilac, the hope flooded out of Luna. She was low again.

She cupped some of the water in her hands, bringing it to her mouth so she could taste the sweetness. It made her laugh, and then it made her hiccup. Her star was gone, but the letters would soon come again.

Until then, Luna sat in her pool of luminescent despair. Laughter flowed from her, and her head was light. Light and fluffy and deep in the clouds of heartbreak.

Charlotte Tunks

A List of the Tragic and Awkward Things I Did Instead of Just Saying "I Love You"

1. I pretended to have watched *Quadrophenia* so I could keep talking to you. Then streamed it the next night in case we had a follow-up conversation.

2. I sorted my packet of Love Hearts sweets so I could fix which one you would pick.

3. I created a fake research trip to the town you moved to so I could visit, even though it was a 500-mile round trip.

4. I liked all your social media posts with the heart emoji.

5. I ate your favourite burger at your favourite restaurant so I could validate your opinion on it later.

6. I learnt all the lyrics to Green Day's *Dookie* album because you said you liked one song from it.

7. I bought a book called *The History of Hull (2ⁿᵈ edition)* purely because I saw it on your bedside table. The edition was important, so that we had the same book covers.

8. I haunted random events at your local pub in case you'd show up.

9. I wore a curated collection of zombie-related t-shirts because you love horror movies.

10. I wrote a piece for an anthology in the hope it would get published and you would think I was cool.

Natalie Toy

I Could Never Be a Mother

I had a dream where I was pregnant. My stomach was clear. You could see the embryo grow, sucking the nutrients out of me. You could see the umbilical cord tied to me so tight and connected I couldn't move freely. My body was able to show people what they previously never understood nor wanted to speak about. The permanence of this creation started in the womb. Its hands and feet pushed from the inside wanting room, trying to burst me, not realising I was protecting it from the outside world.

And when they are in the world they continue to push. They disobey. My future daughter will do what I did because I did what my mother did, despite her telling me not to do it. I'd want to protect my own daughter so badly that I would hurt her. Like a child not knowing when to stop watering a plant, too full of love to realise they are drowning it. I'd fear the potential danger so much that I would then fear I was the danger. Scared I'd drop, drown, neglect, hurt her. I would refuse to hold her, too delicate and fragile, scared I'd mould her wrong, leave the imprint of my touch on her jelly-like head. I'd want to hold her so tightly no one else could ever touch her, scared the wrong person will leave their imprint on her. I'm scared I'd hold onto her too tightly, crushing her little bones, destroying the structure I had built.

I'm scared she'd be too much like me... maybe I just don't want to be a mother to someone like me. I'd push her away. I'm scared I'd treat her how I treat myself. I'd look at her in disgust and disgrace if she was too angry, too competitive, too stubborn. Too much like me for me ever to like her. Too full of my flaws for her ever to be perfect.

In my dream everyone finally realised why I had feared pregnancy and motherhood for so long. They understood my disgust of having a being inside of me, it being tied to me for life. If I was a mum, I'd want to be a good one, but I can't promise that I wouldn't run.

I'd like to think these thoughts are as natural as giving life but it's all alien. How am I meant to feel love for something that I haven't yet met, nor know, something that's not even a full human being when it's squirming inside of me.

I told my friend my dream and he looked at me as if I was sick in the head and said I shouldn't say any of this. He joked that I needed help. Maybe I do. Maybe I don't. Maybe I just don't want to be a mother, and society is sick for pressuring women to fulfil this role. Maybe mothers need more help. Maybe I'm just a naïve twenty-year-old girl who's defiantly young and impulsive, uncommitted, too angry at the world to bring a child into it. Maybe that will change. Maybe it won't. Maybe this should be spoken about.

I could never be a mother.

Polly Reed

In a Meeting. Can't Speak.

The airless room is stuffy with its history –
past prodigies glare down smugly from the walls.
Silent, we wait his imminent arrival.
He's late.

The chairman commences, we listen to each other
politely taking turns to speak.
Decisions made, actions noted, minutes passed.

The door bursts open, ricochets off its' hinge.
A striding tempest flings his bag to the floor, dialogue stops.
We stare at the performance.
He wails – *I couldn't find a parking spot.*

Hushed as his soliloquy drums on,
voice raised, words flying –
inconvenient, waste, more important, my time

Tongue-tied we watch and shuffle in our seats.
Heads down, eyes lowered.
A clapperboard cough from the chair, papers rattle.

Cue meeting restart – it resumes
where it left off, dialogue
disjointed now.

She sits at the end of the long dark table chair furthest from
     the door,
eyes wide at the scene. Holding her breath she expects –
someone to intervene, astounded when no one does.
Boldly she dares clear her throat – *Excuse me*

Heads pivot excitedly, wide-eyed we sit up in our seats
and wait. Brooding the chairman turns, peers over spectacles
and fixes her with an iced stare.

Thank you, my dear, not now. Let's move on.
Heads down, eyes low we shuffle –
back into our uncomfortable places.

Kathryn Winburn

i bite at the hand that feeds me

Don't wear black with brown. Go to sleep in pyjamas, only.

Don't fold the corner of your book. Pour the cereal before the milk.

Wake up in the morning and sleep at night. Make children before you die.

Have a dream the moment you can think. Spit your toothpaste in the sink.

Don't mix alcohols when you drink. Blue is for boys, girls will have pink.

Answers must be written in black ink. Your hairy body is the reason you stink.

What makes you think that I will remain in synch with you? What makes you think that every line,

Will rhyme?

What makes you think I won't dress as a clown? What makes you think?

What makes you think is not them.

They are not you, you are not them.

I am not them. I am not you. Do not put me in the same category as you.

Curse all you do-gooders and clones.

All you neat liners who hate chicken scratch.

All you adults who can't dream like children.

All you geniuses who punish fools.

I will be the ripple that breaks you all.

I will be the kintsugi in your shattered visage.

I will be the misplaced tile.

I will be the desire path.

Your rules cannot contain me

And

neither

can

your

lines

:

)

'Kintsugi' is the Japanese art of repairing broken pottery with lacquer infused with a powdered precious metal, usually gold.

Klaudia Ksiazkiewicz

The Lies We Tell Ourselves

Two knocks at the door. A pause. Then a third. I know who it is. The pause is more for my benefit then his. Immediately after the third knock on my bedroom door he invades my privacy. Elias never waits for an answer, he strolls in as if this were his own room and lounges on the bed.

I drop the pen from my hand onto the desk and close the notebook I was writing in, encasing the words within. Elias stares up at the ceiling, giving the impression that he isn't aware of everything that's going on in the room. He enjoys playing these games. Enjoys telling the lies that fall so effortlessly from his lips. I've spent years creating my stories, weaving a web that's become so entangled that I have to remind myself who I am sometimes. Here is what I've learnt along the way: our lies rip us open and leave blood pooling at our feet. They take hold of our throats and squeeze. They suffocate us. They're embedded into the walls to look at as we walk by, demanding to be acknowledged. Our unspoken words have left us twisted and broken.

Over the last few years, I've forgotten what is real. Every other word that pours from my lips is a lie. A beautiful, twisted lie. Ones perfectly sculpted for who they're made for.

For Elias, lying is as easy as breathing. So, we play this game where he pretends not to be aware of my every breath, every rustle of clothing, every nervous tap of my foot against the floor.

I look at him, waiting. I won't give into these games we force ourselves to play. Eventually, he turns his eyes to me. A small sense of triumph fills me, he rarely lets me win the game of who speaks first. We ask ourselves, *who is willing to tarnish themselves further?*

"You look lovely this evening," he says softly. His face is impassive and I know that's the first lie he will tell me tonight.

"Why are you here, Elias?" I try to keep my tone neutral.

To torment you. To make your life miserable. Is what he doesn't say. "That's a broad question. I'm in this house because our parents decided to get married."

"You know that's not what I was asking. Why are you in my room, *right now?*" He makes a show of checking his watch, straightening the strap.

"Oh right, dinner's ready". He stands and strolls out of my room without another word.

* * *

"Pass the potatoes" my mother's husband asks. *Get out of my house*, is what he really wants to say. My mother and I moved with her husband and his son two years ago. Neither my new stepfather or stepbrother seemed thrilled about the situation. My stepfather wanted to live separately, but mum insisted. She has an uncanny ability to get everything she wants. I both respect and resent her for it. From the moment we moved in the lies began, the undercurrent of hate and words left unspoken running like live electricity through the house.

"Of course." I say and pass over the potatoes.

"*Dad.*" Mum snaps. "Of course, *Dad,*" she reiterates.

"Sorry, *Dad,*" I say just to satisfy her. Two years of living under the same roof as my stepfather and everything I've learnt is from observation only. He wakes every day at six, goes to his personal gym. Has breakfast with my mum at seven-thirty, only because *she* insists. By eight he's in his office and stays there until five, unless he has in-person meetings, which are rare. We all have dinner at seven, which *he* insists we do. Every distinguished family eats dinner together *every day,* no matter of age, apparently.

I look over at Elias, who appears to be eating his food. He is the spitting image of his father. Dark brown hair. Blue eyes. His parents see one side of him while I see another. He antagonises me on a daily basis. The angrier I get the more humorous he finds it. He remains calm while I'm shaking with barely repressed rage. I've never understood why he hates me, why he takes so much joy in finding all my insecurities and exposing them.

"How was school today?" My mother's husband asks Elias and me. *I don't care about you,* are his unspoken words. I can imagine scenes like this differently: just when I've filled my plate with food, my stepfather would pick up my plate and throw it against the wall. Gravy would drip down the wallpaper. Next the food on the table would be wiped away with a sweep of his hands. Then, he would storm over, wrap his hands around my throat and strangle me until I pass out. Elias would just sit there watching, his chin propped up on a hand. Mum would do absolutely nothing.

"It was good." I tell him. He just nods and looks at Elias.

He takes his eyes off me to look at his father. "It was good, too."

"Have you joined the football team?"

"No, not yet." Elias shows slight irritation at this question. Mum, sat next to me, remains silent.

"Generations of men in our family have been a part of the football team at your school. I expect you not to break that tradition."

Elias taps his finger on the table. *I hate football*, I think Elias wants to tell his father. "Of course, I'll do it tomorrow." *I won't be doing any such thing, tomorrow*. He goes back to eating his food. Not quite eating, just pushing his food around his plate, seemingly unbothered by the topic of conversation.

Despite Elias' hate towards me, I notice things about him. Things that make me want to sympathise. Like me, he loves to read. It's rare I find him without a book in his hand. At our family dinners he doesn't eat much and avoids conversation with his father and my mother. He obviously hates football and avoids joining the team as much as possible, despite being under pressure from his dad. There's a lot of pressure on Elias to join his father's company when he graduates, even though he hates business. I doubt he even knows the first thing about his father's company. I push back against his aloof nature, but only so far.

Abruptly, my mother's husband stands from the table and leaves. Dinner is over, apparently. Mum trails behind, without a word to me.

I fill my plate with more food and stand to leave.

"You know, you're doing it all wrong," Elias tells me, his own plate remaining untouched.

"Doing what wrong?" I look out of the dining room window,

unable to look him in the eyes when I speak to him. "You're intelligent, I'm sure you'll figure it out." As he leaves, I think to myself that might be the first truthful thing he's told me in years.

Shannon Walton

Gossip

On the first day of class, we had to tell the person sitting next to us what our favourite animal was. You told me that yours was a giraffe. Before I had the chance to respond, the teacher spoke, and we didn't interact much after that.

I would sometimes see you in the halls and the corridors. We both acquired different groups of friends, and we didn't share any lessons because we were always one or two sets apart in every subject. Your first boyfriend had asked my best friend out the week before.

After school, he began working in a restaurant three miles away. He hated it at first because the other guys there would talk down to him, forgetting that they were once in his place. He started going to the gym religiously, I'm not sure that you'd even recognise him now, he bulked up to ensure that he took up more space. He also started drinking nightly, I heard, weekdays as well as weekends. People don't regularly see him sober, even on shift he secretly drinks in the locker room and serves customers with questionable, over-enthused happiness that fades when he is out of sight. They say his manager hasn't spotted him doing this yet, but I think she probably has, she just turns a blind eye to it because deep down she knows he performs better after he's had a drink.

She inherited the restaurant from her father. It wasn't her goal in life, I was told, but because the restaurant was so successful it would have been stupid of her not to take it on after his passing. However now, the building is starting to feel neglected. The paint near the bathrooms peels and the Christmas lights that were hung up four years ago are now a permanent fixture in the decor, flickering sickly blues and greens. She is great at putting a smile on with customers, but she finds holding staff down difficult. I've heard some former employees say she can be bossy and unpleasant behind the scenes. In a way, it makes sense, because I was told that before taking on the restaurant she wanted to be a lawyer: strong, outspoken, a high level of self-importance. But whenever I have seen her there are huge bags under her eyes, probably from the late nights she spends looking after her young son, who was an accident, by the way. A product of one of the chefs and an evening of drinking after a busy Saturday shift. He is naughty in school. He has to be taken care of by a babysitter most nights because of his mum's working hours. He doesn't have one consistent babysitter; most of them grow sick of his screaming and recklessness. He has a hard time trusting adults, I think, because there is no sense of permanency in his life. He never knows who will be picking him up from the school gate, making him dinner, ironing his uniform, helping him into his pyjamas. He does have a knack for drawing, though. He's only five and already knows not to draw the eyes on a face at the top of the head, but in the middle, to allow the correct proportions for the forehead and eyebrows too. He probably doesn't understand the technical side of this, but there is definitely something interesting about a child who can draw. I've heard that he draws all of his babysitters, in garish colours much like the eternal Christmas lights in the restaurant. The loveliest drawing, however, is the one of his teacher. He has gifted her long, flowing hair and twinkling eyes, eyes that are in the middle of the head, I should say.

Teaching was the perfect career choice for her because she loves children. You might think this is a given, but a lot of teachers do not actually care about the children personally, only collectively, or when they are in formation. But she really loves children; she loves how they aren't afraid to ask questions, and even the quietest, shyest of children have minds capable of the biggest imagination. She had a wonderful childhood herself, I'm told, one that was full of swings, party bags and shoes that flashed when she stomped her foot on the ground. Her own nostalgia of childhood fed into the way she acted with children because she knew that they would remember every kind or harsh word that she spoke to them. For example, she will never forget how one time she was blamed for stealing another student's coat when she was only six, when in fact, the other student had hung it up on the tree near the car park and blamed her for its absence on purpose. She remembers how guilty she had been made to feel for something she hadn't done, so she knew even more than others how important it was to be understanding. Her love for children had created an even more desperate longing for her wanting her own, but her partner was unsure. For her, being unsure was as good as no, because she wanted to bring up her own child in a world where two hearts had wished for it to exist.

He can't stand the thought of having children with her because he is in love with somebody else. It happened not too long ago, the old-fashioned way. It unravelled like a movie scene which is what he had always wanted. There she was, struggling to reach a factory-made cake from the top shelf in the bakery aisle, and there he was, armed and ready to grab it for her. She was so grateful, too grateful, in fact, an invitation for him to continue the conversation with her so he could witness her flash another smile at him. He complimented her taste in cake, which led to him complimenting her dress and lipstick two weeks later in a quiet bar. They meet on Wednesday nights. She has a husband too. She says the love died years ago, as does he, but with each other, they feel like teenagers again, as if anything is possible. To avoid being spotted, they go to that run-down restaurant, the one with the stale Christmas lights that people avoid because of the tired-looking manager and reused menu. There is another thing that keeps them going back, though, the smiley waiter who smells a little of alcohol and has a huge spring in his step for a weekday night.

That waiter, of course, remembers you as his first girlfriend, even though he asked my best friend out first. I caught up with him recently, he served me when I decided to grab something to eat there. We talked about people from school and we speculated on their futures. He mentioned you, actually. He said to me that you'd opened a nursery, and that you were expecting your first child. He said you can't miss the nursery, because of the huge giraffe signpost that sticks out the side of the building and casts a funny shadow onto the streets. He said he thinks it's you, anyway, he can't be sure. I told him it will be. He smiled after that, and took my plate away.

Anna Edwards

aww's! O, me? I'm fine...

I

A new human continent arose. Released from a sea of sounds, reverberating and repeating on the tide of waves shaped around thoughts condensed into a series of long drawn out *r*'s in every corner of the room.

R – The sound of deflating sympathy. A moment of transparency when rooms can see through you and everyone looks around as they no longer know what to say.

U – lost in the space between being in the room and a million miles away. Tethered to a long line of thoughts stretching outwards to the unknown answer like musical notes that bore through speakers that urgently try to sound human as all distant songs are heard deafened. Being flattened by the shock of the small circle of friends. The hug that feels empty where it would usually fill. The evening slows as the time of being insubstantial grows. Walking across a room with everyone looking for the damage.

O – the open mouthed hollow realisation, in sounds thought but unsaid, unheard but shared somehow in their unexplored depths. O, like looking towards the tunnel of the future seeing brightness in the distant circle and appreciating the dark surrounding void of human sympathy. The distillation of hollowed out meaning forms around the contemporary sound of acceptance:

K

Fragile   ?   popularity
foundations of sand in   our thought-filled palace of art
Vanity gone left with the images on walls running around the
boundaries of space in the open mouth of glasses upon a table
chasing thoughts around your head – that spiral out – into a
vortex concentrated on the hole of perception in your vision –
becoming only a visual image – alone with defiance holding up
empty words against defeat in pride.

Drinking in the empty glass and feeling the boundaries fade
into the smudged senses of taste and the internal touch of a
burnt out alcohol-fuelled shame. A bottle becomes another
bottle, a shot, give it another shot, along with the tail end of
an unwanted choice...

                              ...standing out, in the cold
                                          then outside
                                          in the dark.

II

a round,
a pint, or two,
a couple of celebratory drinks
to wash away the idea of being supported.
Not being up to the toast. Moved along the bar.
Watching the long pint in gulps of dread.
Tomorrow's bad head with work to do.
A jelly shot. The empty glass again.   Goodbyes in a rush.
              The   street
                    empty   the night stretches out,
                                    with thoughts and feelings
                    unravelling around the ways of life in agitation.

III

Getting home, hanging up the smart outfit in a creased heap on the floor. Home, where the armour of outside ideas can lie, resting, and be replaced by the plain loungewear of uncomfortable truth. Any frame of achievement resting upon the wall can come down and such results pass on as someone's work in time past that made you stronger today. That time is lost. They spoke, but more did not speak than those that can be heard, or seen as pride converts to disappointed hope in one sound. "Aww" cannot be unspoken as much as it cannot be unheard.

It's a shame that no one's words sounded good. Consolation withholds the release of suspended truth that springs about the well intentioned talk of opportunities.

The days will speak with unsaid thoughts. The rest is welcome, as now everyone is free to go without thought.

Oh...

Everything is...   awesome.

Me?   I'm fine!

OK.   Enough said.

Stui

The Regret Afterwards

You start moving a mile a day because it is good for you. Sometimes – mostly – on a treadmill in the comfort of your mum's garage, but you allow yourself the privilege of a *real walk* on the sunnier days when your bones can stand it. You drink ten glasses of water a day, with ice. You transfer your seventh into a water bottle and shake it by fellow pedestrians so that *you* know that *they* know you're drinking it. You scoff inwardly at the children drinking Fanta and Coca-Cola; at the mothers and fathers who trail sluggishly behind them, cigarette or greasy sandwich in-hand. You know they could never match your newfound pace. You smile at them, because you have always been kind.

At home, you shower with cold water to get your circulation running. Your "friend", who you had met online three weeks previous, told you it was an excellent way to *"burn off the excess"*. You hate it, but you do it anyway. Your mother spends two hours cooking you a meal from scratch, and you discard one quarter of it in the kitchen bin, and three quarters in the bathroom.

When your period comes around, you rest a hot water bottle on your stomach and drink an excessive amount of green tea. When the bottle cools down, you utilise the warmth of your empty mug. They both grow cold eventually, and you suffer while the kettle boils. You rest your fingers inches away from the stream to evade the unusual coldness of your house. Your mother asks if you would, *please*, consider Paracetamol, but you don't think it's worth it. A calorie is a calorie, after all.

You post a photo, before a gathering with family-friends, of you wearing that lovely yellow dress. The one that starts just above your breasts and ends just below your thighs. The size small. You have never known a size small, not since adolescence. You caption the photo: *'why do I look so sad?'* and the comments flood with anecdotes about how attractive your friends think you are. You receive a direct message from a random man who had casually followed you during sixth-form, but had likely paid you no mind. *You're pretty,* he says, and for once, you try to believe him.

At the gathering, your mother's friends fawn over you. The lights are bright, and harsh, and you feel naked. You hide yourself away in the furthest, least populated corner of the room. You scrunch yourself up, trying to make yourself small. Smaller.

What's your secret, sweetheart?
You look wonderful!
How I miss my eighteen-year-old metabolism!
I'm so glad you've started taking care of yourself.
Your hair looks beautiful! I've never known you to dress up!
Look at your waist! Someone's been laying off the cake...

You treat yourself to a drink. Then another. Then another.

You cry in the taxi home.

In your first week of university, you buy a pretty blue bowl. It is the length of your wrist to the tip of your middle finger, and the width of your thumb to your pinkie. You serve all your meals in here, exclusively.

Your mother calls you daily to ask if you're eating, and you tell her *yes*. This is true to an extent, and you relish in her relief. She never asks *how much* or *what* or *when*. You are an honest person – a part of yourself that you have grown to resent – and you think she may be afraid of your answer.

A few hours ago.
Yesterday.
I can't remember.

The mirrors add cellulite that you refuse to claim. You live in the corners of your bedroom, evading eye and physical contact, lest you be perceived too intricately. You treat your body like your greatest friend and your cruellest foe. Never before have you loved and despised yourself so intensely.

In your second year of study, you meet somebody. Suddenly, you're loved romantically. Incomprehensibly. There is a sudden softness in your bones, and limbs, and heart. You eat because *they* do – because *they* want you to. They make you meals in their large, shared kitchen, serving you things you haven't eaten in years, in bowls much larger than your hand. There is an instant, unusual closeness between the two of you. A warm domesticity that isn't typical between such strangers.

Food becomes complex, not only in a physical sense, but also conceptually. For the first seventeen years of your life, food was your lover, your backbench, your therapist. More recently, it was your enemy, the very bane of your existence. Now, somehow, it is both. Your bowls and plates encapsulate a younger self, one that loves and indulges. She reaches out a small, plump hand, and drags your throat to the bottom. You're elated, drowning in *happy relationship weight*, until the very second your plate is clear. Then, you're forced to sit with the ever-encompassing weight of the regret afterwards. There is *always* regret afterwards. No matter what you eat. No matter how you age.

Everything has its number, its weight, its gravity. It does not matter what it is. It does not matter that you *do*, in fact, eat it. You wonder what *your* number would be. How many days would it take to eat you? How many people could you feed? How much would a person weigh if they ate you whole?

At lunch with friends you hide beneath a parasol, in the furthest and darkest shade from the bustling pavements, scrunching your limbs into yourself. You smile politely when addressed, your voice always much larger and louder than you would like. You feel the cold sleekness of the restaurant's cutlery, the sharpness of it. You take notice of the weight of your calzone, and the weight of your tongue. Twelve months ago, you would have feigned illness to escape. You would have bagged up half and binned it at home. You would have picked and prodded until you had mutilated your enemy to a disgusting mush. Not anymore. You know this now to be a silent battle. The delicious concoction of tomato and bread, herbs and cheese, hits the back of your throat, and a young part of you is warm, and happy, and healthy.

Yet, in the midday crowd, basking in the sunlight with remarkable pride, is a slightly younger, much thinner girl. She sees you every day, three times, sometimes more. You mostly ignore her: a skill that you have meticulously nurtured within yourself. Yet, you know that she is embedded far too deeply for this to be sustainable. When you aren't craving food, you're craving her. You spend your quiet time relaying the delicate intricacies of her shadow.

With sharp, hidden disgust, she shakes her water bottle, and smiles.

Amelia Rodgers

Six Lines

Six lines. Too straight. Too aware. They are freshly drafted in congealing red on pale flesh.

Six lines. Too damaged. Too raw. Most refuse to keep reading, afraid of how they might end.

Six lines. Too mute. Too forlorn. They are frustrated that with such short scores they cannot say more.

Six lines. Too distant. Too deep. They are too shallow to scratch the surface of what they speak.

Six lines. Too shamed. Too shy. They were written to be read but expect to be silenced instead.

Six lines that say they may take you away. But that is not for you to worry about. Not today.

Julie Bennett

Durga's Spoken Words

I sat and listened to Daadi Maa
as she rubbed milk over my body
a natural method to lighten the skin
to be fair is to be beautiful she would say
I repeated this to myself daily
more than a mantra.

I bleached my skin at the age of 12
I bleached my hair at the age of 16
I bleached my heritage at the age of 18
to be fair is to be beautiful.

every night I would meet myself
tears soothing my burnt skin
asking my reflection why was I not born white
the power held in these spoken words
destroyed me from the outside in
all I wanted was to be

                    beautiful.

                        Escaping to the forest
            the trees held no judgement of my skin
                            I lay in the soil
                        re-reading the Gita
                        signifying my needs
                    for Shiva's expectations of me
            I gather daisies to decorate my chunni
                    and meet Durga who tells me

in sarees of silk or cotton worn
stands a woman whose skin glows from the sun
dark hair wraps her body in protection
a heritage that holds ancestors' stories
like monsoon showers painting the sky with bold hues
women are the golden hands that come after the rain
casting a brighter day

these are the unspoken words you must speak to your sisters.

Manisha Dhesi

Spiritcalling

I walk into the House of Trembling Madness just after seven on a Saturday evening. One of my closest friends, Tarryn, is turning thirty tomorrow. It's busy, all of the tables downstairs are filled with strangers and the queue for the bar is spilling over. I walk upstairs and remember the quasi-gothic feel of the place, the animal skulls, the classical paintings, the mood(y) lighting. I can't find them upstairs either. I double check the Facebook event. Forty-four minutes ago, Tarryn's mum updated the venue to Lendal Cellars.

It's late February. There's no utterance of spring in the air as I walk down the uneven cobbled street, unsure where these cellars are. I search for this unknown world on Google maps. You haven't messaged me back. It's fine, you said we *might* see each other tonight. You're out with some friends as well. I don't know where though.

I find the cellars. More mood lighting, but brighter. The brick walls and low ceilings create the ghostly feel that is inherent to York. The old buildings are like mausoleums, erected long before I arrived here and filled with the residue of footsteps that still reside within. I find Tarryn and her friends and family. I hand her a birthday card. She thanks me and puts it into her bag. I greet the other people I know in the group before I go to the bar. There's information written on the wall behind the bar detailing the history of the building. It was once a Friary which held a large library, and was turned into a wine cellar in the 18th century. No further words are written about the thousands of lost books. You haven't messaged me back yet. The wall does continue though, saying that human remains were found at the site and some guests claim to have seen a monk-like figure in the lower seating area. I buy a double Jack and coke and sit opposite Tarryn and her partner Andy.

It's not long after the pandemic. We walk down the stairs of a house converted into an Italian restaurant. I can't remember if the waiter wears a mask or not as he leads me and Eleanor to the table. It's just big enough for two and next to the wall. There's a candle in a small glass vase. It's quaint and just quiet enough for it to be romantic. We chat and eat. By this time in the relationship, I'm a whisper of who I was when we first met. I'm starting to turn inwards. I'm not so present or talkative. But we can't be too far down that road to inevitability because Eleanor tells me a secret. Something she has never told anyone before. She says she doesn't know where that came from or why she told me. I say something in response, but I can't remember what.

Andy and I talk about video games for twenty minutes. More people have turned up, some of whom I know, and Tarryn is doing the rounds. Other friends from university have turned up and they sit near me. I try to engage Sophie in conversation but I don't get much from her. I run out of questions. Anna and Kuba sit a little further away from me. They sit next to someone they don't know. They don't speak to him for all the time they are there. Phone signal is interrupted at best. You haven't texted me. You said you would let me know where you were. I think about messaging you but it's difficult to get the balance between being forward and being a friend when you have a partner and you're trying to fix the relationship. All I can do is try to hold my tongue, put my phone down, and wait. It's cool. You're with your friends having a good time.

Three nights ago, we were drunk and giggly in the Student Union and then the library. We said many more-than-friendly things that we probably shouldn't have said. But now, I can't say how I want to find you somewhere in York, in a bar or on the street, and be drunk and giggly again. How I want to hold you close. How I want to breathe you in. There's a question I want to ask you after something you said on that tipsy mid-week night.

I'm sitting in Elliott's garden on a not-quite-chilly evening in early February. I'm here often. We drink cups of tea and talk to each other, to the stars. We've known each other for five years or so and he's my closest friend but tonight, he reveals something I didn't know about him. He tells me, and the stars, that when he started uni, he was seeing a girl. He tells me that she ghosted him, and two weeks later, he found out via social media that she had a boyfriend.

We see each other next Wednesday. You ask me about my

night, I say it was alright. I say it was alright because we stayed in one place and it was just alright. I don't say that it was just alright because I checked my phone all night. I don't say that it was just alright because I was aware of its muteness in my pocket all night. I ask in return. You say you had fun. After five aching hours, I leave Lendal Cellars with Tarryn and Andy. We walk through town and chat. We part at the corner of Goodramgate and Lord Mayor's Walk. I hug them both. I walk home slowly without checking my phone. I'm willing it to vibrate in my pocket. But, it doesn't move or talk, it's just a weight, a silence, a haunting. I get to bed at half twelve. Usually, I leave my phone at the end of my bed, out of reach. Tonight, it sleeps on the little shelf that lines the bed frame. I turn it off silent. You message me at half two, apologising, and saying that you have gone home. I had already been asleep for an hour.

Josh Brittain

I'm Fine

Sometimes I'm so angry that I scare myself.
Sometimes I'm too mellow for my own good.
I'm constantly alone.
Dancing in the dark with the devil in my head.
And I need help to get him out.
The last thing I want is to be a burden,
or even worse,
to show a sign of weakness.
I feel my eyes are causing my mask to slip.
They are telling them what my mouth cannot.
They express my need for a shoulder or an ear,
But this is my weight to carry.
I cannot let myself drag the people
I love under this downpour.
I cannot. I will not.
But, what if that's the point?
What if taking their welcoming hands
or accepting their umbrella so we can stand under it
together is what I'm supposed to do?
Maybe, this is no time to fall on my sword   *"I'm fine."*
for the sake of heroic stoicism.
Maybe, at last, a partner
to carry this weight,
is long overdue.
Maybe, someone else can part the clouds
of this thunderstorm following me around.
Maybe it's a discussion for another day.

Elliot Scriven

Awelon

She is a soft-spoken spirit, hailing from beautiful, forgotten places. You must listen if you wish to hear her. Thoughts trail from her skirts as she soars, riding currents to ring out of thunderstorms and smooth troubled waters as she passes. Her voice is touched with salted winds and early snows, flowers from far shores. You hear it flutter in the long grass surrounding old ruins and lonely oaks, speaking in the wind-blistered shells of leaves and the gaps between stones with speckled moss. It is lyrical and nonsensical, words beyond words hiding in birdsong, the sway of trees, litter chasing leaves down dilapidated streets. Her words hide in thoughts as Awelon plants kisses on the nape of your neck.

Some weeks back, I heard her on a mountain. Me and my family had gone to bury my Taid's ashes at his favourite lunch spot, a lake crowned by sky and old stones. She circled us lightly as we read his favourite hymn, carrying the words over the water to crest the cloud-wreathed peak above. Her own song trailed us through the grass on the walk down, clusters of green blades whistling to her current as trees murmured on the steep valley.

I think back to the wordless comforts on the mountain, Awelon speaking easily of memory and love as she danced up the valley walls, skipping over waterfalls to slide down trees. I think my Taid will be happy where he is, listening to ravens and the wind playing on the lake.

I miss my Grandad and Taid in scales beyond words; sometimes it feels very difficult to be in a world without them. I remember my Grandad by his proud roses and the myriad of playtime me and my sister got out of his shed. My Taid was gentle but strong – he had built his own drystone wall in a tiny Welsh village and showed the same loving patience when we gave him pretend haircuts as children.

I think of them when Awelon brushes past on my walks, smelling of distant storms and new seasons. To hear her, to feel her, is to see them both again. Unspoken she goes, weaving memory and loss into peace as she passes through the trees.

Ewan Scott

The Oversoul

The river's course is winding. We are lost,
walking upstream, weighed down by our baggage.
For a long time we talked
about nothing, our words empty and meaningless,
punctuated by sighs.
The source seems forever out of sight,
known only by the flight of water and the uphill trek.
We've often said the source is lost
or inaccessible. Guarded
by rocks amongst these glowing mountains.

We've brought distraction on our journey. Speech
covering over the unspoken.
"I remember... I remember...
I am... I am...
I... I... I... I..."
These words are the roots of our dissatisfaction.

What sent us to wander afar?
Source of drowning and of nourishment
found in every drop of water. We utter these words,
unspoken before. We
who now walk with water. As we look
deep into the currents,
churning, churning, changing,
sons of currents gone before.

Our journey is over. We meet the source
in every drop of water
and in our feet moving slowly up the bank
for there is no I that wanders
Through this infinite river. The endless illusions
are silenced now.

This is the spirit of the universe,
a refuge from all fear.

Matthew Howell

Acknowledgements

The Editorial and Production Team wish to thank all those who submitted writing and artwork to this year's anthology for their creativity, collaboration and trust. Thanks are due also to Rob O'Connor for his management of the project and invaluable guidance throughout. Thank you to John Challis and Caleb Klaces for contributing your time and words to the Foreword and blurb. To the Marketing and Events Team, thank you for creating a community around the anthology through the hugely successful student showcase and launch events. Thank you to the Blogs and Podcasting Team for promoting the anthology and involving people from across the Creative Writing faculty.

Cover and blurb design by Ollie Groover
My Lady of Grace illustration by Lyn Robertson
Illustrations on pages 60 & 61 by Liza Pink Dangerfield

The Editorial and Production Team
Erin Blaney; Ollie Groover; Amy Platt; Ethan Clark;
Angelina Turner; Jenny-Rose Morrison; Laura Beddow;
Amelie Woodwards; Rhiannon Thorley; Harry Parkin;
Merryn Lynn; Sophia Murphy; Charlie Wreford-Doree;
Lucy Summers; Cara Evans; Elsie Lonsdale, Allie Odabas.

Marketing and Events Team
Sebastian Forrester; Thea Moore; Amy Wyeth;
Abbey McKenna; Millie Oliver; Arwen Tipling; Ellie Surridge;
Eloise Stone; Sophie Mann; Charlotte Stoker.

Blogs and Podcasting Team
Rachel Bentley; Claire Huya, Ryan Williams; Tom Banks;
Ben Howsam; Owen Brett; Tallullah Sykes; Phoebe Rodgers.